CONTENTS

Published 2022.

Little Brother Books Ltd, Ground Floor,
23 Southernhay East, Exeter, Devon EX1 1QL
books@littlebrotherbooks.co.uk | www.littlebrotherbooks.co.uk

The Little Brother Books trademark, email and website addresses, are the sole and exclusive properties of Little Brother Books Limited.

Shoot! is a registered trademark and used under license by Little Brother Books Ltd. ©2022 Pedigree Toys and Brands Limited.

Printed in the United Kingdom.

Images used under license © Pro Sports Images ltd and © Offside Sports Photography.

While care has been taken to ensure that information is considered to be true and correct at the date of publication, changes in circumstances after the time of publication may impact on the accuracy of the information.

ALL ABOUT ME!

Before we meet the players, let's discover everything about you!

Just fill in the answers to the questions below and, in years to come, you can look back and smile at your responses...

NAME Izzy

MY TOP 3 PLAYERS!

1. Ella toone
2. Alessia russo
3. Leah willsom

MY BEST FOOTBALL MOMENT... AND WHY!

My best Football moment was probly when England woman won the euros and lifed the cup.

Isabella Hough-king   H.King H. II

THE TEAM I PLAY FOR

MY POSITION

right wing ♡

I WANT TO PLAY LIKE... AND WHY!

I want to play like alessia russo
because the back heel
was a blast to scor like that.

MY OWN PLAYER RATINGS!

Give yourself a mark out of five for the categories below by colouring in each star. Try to be honest so you know what areas of your game you can improve.

SHOOTING 4/5

PASSING 4/5

TACKLING 5/5

TEAMWORK 3/5

SKILL 4/5

KIT ME OUT!

Here's your chance to design a new strip for the team you support. Don't hold back – this is a fantasy kit so anything goes!

SCRAMBLED STARS!

ANSWERS ON PAGE 47

Below are six Lionesses. We have scrambled the names of our EURO 2022 heroes – all you have to do is figure out who they are.

1

MEH PALE RUN

_____

2

RAMY SPEAR

Mary eaps

3

E LOOT LANE

Ella toore

4

THE NEW LLIE

Ellen white

5

ME KIDS TOES

_____

6

LEEN OX WORD AGE

_____

GIRL POWER!

THE TIMELINE OF

1920

December 26th, more than 53,000 packed into Everton's Goodison Park to watch the two top amateur teams in England – Dick, Kerr Ladies and St Helen's Ladies – with more than 10,000 locked out!

1921

The FA ban women's football being played at the grounds of the clubs who are members, saying "the game of football is quite unsuitable for females and ought not to be encouraged." This ban lasts almost 50 years!!

2002

Lily Parr of Dick, Kerr Ladies becomes the first woman to be inducted in the UK's National Football Museum Hall of Fame.

1999

The 1999 World Cup in the USA sees almost 1.2million tickets sold.

2009

The UEFA Women's Cup, which had launched in 2001, becomes the UEFA Women's Champions League.

2010

The Women's Super League is launched in England with 12 professional teams and major sponsorship.

HOW THE GAME HAS GROWN AT HOME AND OVERSEAS IN THE PAST 100 YEARS

WOMEN'S FOOTBALL

1921

Following the ban, the English Ladies Football Association is formed and soon has 58 clubs join as women's football continues to thrive, but without stadiums and suitable facilities, it struggles to progress.

1969

The English Women's FA is formed following increased interest in the game after England men's World Cup win three years before.

1991

The first official FIFA Women's World Cup is held in China and won by the USA who beat Norway 2-1 in the final. The tournament has since been held every four years and USA have won the World Cup a record four times.

1971

Though not yet recognised by FIFA, the first Women's World Cup is held in Mexico, regularly attracting crowds of more than 110,000.

2022

Barcelona's Champions League clash with Real Madrid is watched by a record attendance of 91,553 – the largest number to watch a club match.

2022

EURO 2022 is staged in and won by England. Northern Ireland reach the group stage and the tournament is a resounding success with more than 500,000 fans attending games in total.

SPOT THE BALL

Six balls have appeared in each of these footy photos.
Write down which is the real one for each.

ANSWERS ON PAGE 47

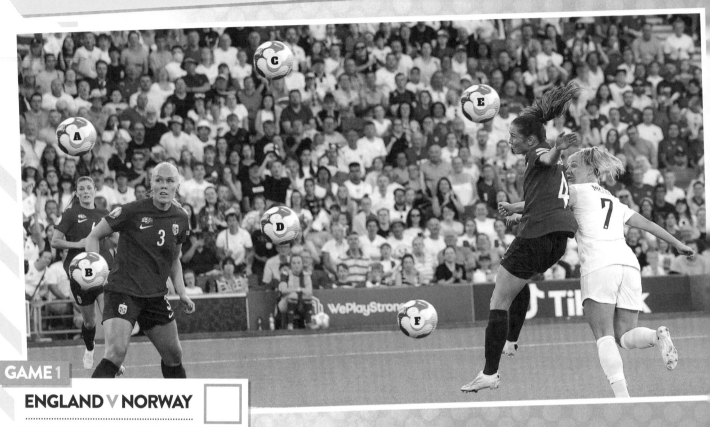

GAME 1

ENGLAND V NORWAY

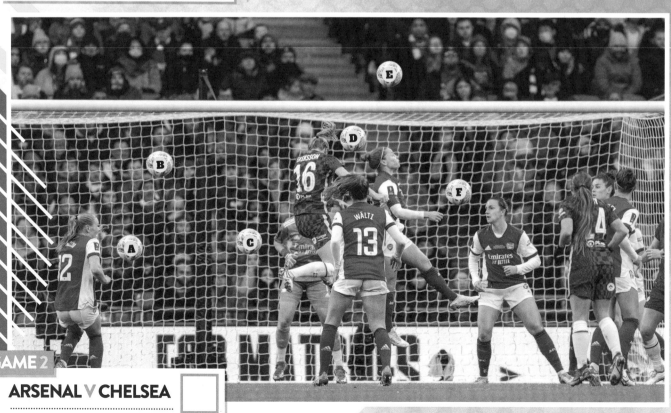

GAME 2

ARSENAL V CHELSEA

GAME 3

NETHERLANDS V SWEDEN

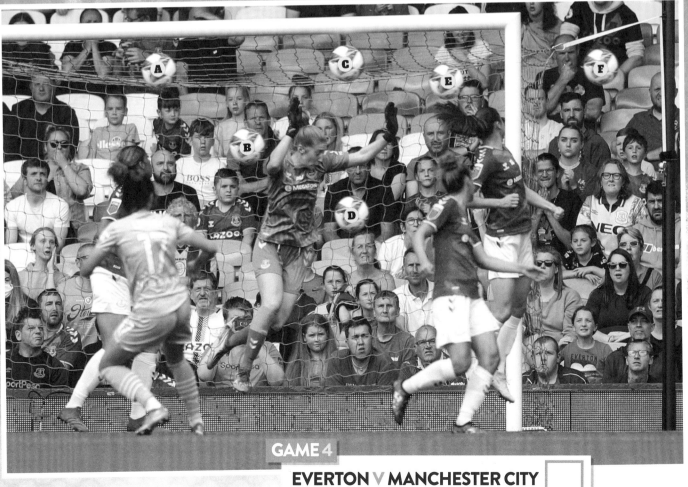

GAME 4

EVERTON V MANCHESTER CITY

MAGIC MEGAN

Everyone knows what a wonderful footballer USA star Megan Rapinoe is. The double World Cup winner can produce magic on the biggest stage, but can you work out which of the five strikes end with the ball in the net?

ANSWERS ON PAGE 47

CHAMPIONS OF EUROPE!

Below are 12 teams that will compete in the 2022/23 Champions League which includes teams that have qualified for the group stages and the earlier qualification rounds. So, let's see how much you know about women's football in Europe!

ANSWERS ON PAGE 47

G	L	E	N	T	O	R	A	N	Y	S	G	O	J	G
D	Y	H	Y	M	C	B	V	R	R	P	N	O	L	B
M	A	N	C	H	E	S	T	E	R	C	I	T	Y	A
A	R	H	W	A	Q	Z	G	C	A	V	S	N	Y	R
P	R	J	U	V	E	N	T	U	S	G	W	Z	T	C
W	O	S	D	W	A	S	P	G	H	D	O	P	I	E
A	N	S	I	E	R	R	D	L	W	B	X	L	N	L
R	S	E	B	N	U	J	C	E	B	E	F	K	A	O
R	Q	X	O	V	A	I	E	A	H	D	S	S	E	N
L	U	R	N	S	T	L	W	A	G	C	B	B	S	A
U	Y	I	C	L	L	J	T	H	Z	Z	U	J	N	O
R	Ç	O	E	N	S	X	S	R	N	M	R	Y	A	M
M	N	C	N	H	A	P	P	A	W	S	G	L	W	W
X	S	P	A	R	T	A	P	R	A	G	U	E	S	B
L	K	B	C	G	J	T	B	R	J	A	L	L	V	I

CELTIC

LYON

BARCELONA

RANGERS

ARSENAL

WOLFSBURG

GLENTORAN

MANCHESTER CITY

JUVENTUS

SWANSEA CITY

CHELSEA

SPARTA PRAGUE

DRAW YOUR
FOOTY HERO!

Sketch your favourite football star, on or off the pitch. Make sure you use some cool colours and make them stand out!

TOP 10

WORLD STARS

So, who are the best of the best in world football? SHOOT set out to find the TOP 10 players on the planet and here's the results...

1 ALEXIA PUTELLAS

Regarded as the best women's footballer in the world, the Barcelona and Spain star is a creative midfielder who assists and scores goals for club and country. The Ballon d'Or Feminin has won over 100 caps for Spain.

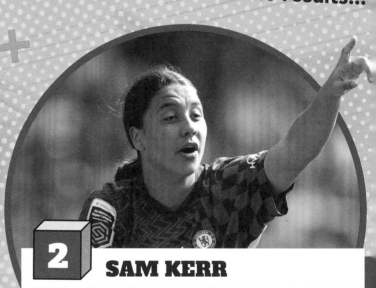

2 SAM KERR

The all-time Australia record goal-scorer and captain, Sam Kerr is the Chelsea goal-machine Footballer Writers' Association Women's Footballer of the Year in 2022. Kerr has the lot – speed, vision, skill and the ability to score goals out of nothing.

3 CATARINA MACARIO

The attacking midfielder was born in Brazil but represents the USA. The shining light of a Lyon side who continually challenge for top prizes, Macario's rise to the top shows no signs of stopping.

4 AITANA BONMATI

The creative midfielder is one of the main reasons Barcelona have become such a force in recent seasons and was voted MVP in the 2021 Champions League final.

5 VIVIANNE MIEDEMA

The exciting Dutch forward plays for Arsenal and is the star of her national team. Tricky, fast and inventive, she is deadly around the box and the current FA WSL's all-time leading scorer.

6 CAROLINE GRAHAM HANSEN

Another Barcelona player to make the top 10. The Norwegian winger is one of women's football's most decorated stars with her intelligence and athleticism making her one of the most exciting forwards in Europe and a superstar in her homeland.

7 MARIE-ANTOINETTE KATOTO

At only 23 years old, the French striker is already Paris Saint-Germain's all-time leading goalscorer. She is fast, powerful, and athletic, so watch out for Katoto in the coming years.

8 WENDIE RENARD

The captain of Lyon and France is the first defender to appear in this top 10. With more than 30 trophies won at Lyon, this experienced, tall and tough-tackling centre-back is rated as one of the best on the planet.

9 LENA OBERDORF

The Wolfsburg midfielder is the only defensive midfielder in our list, combining physicality with a smart footballing brain. She was voted the UEFA Women's EURO 2022 Young Player of the Tournament.

10 DEBINHA MIRI

This technically gifted Brazilian forward combines skill, balance, technique and dribbling which thrills fans. The North Carolina Courage star has won more than 130 caps for her country and at 31, is the veteran of this most talented list of footballers.

SHOOT+
SUPER QUIZ

2022 was a wonderful year for women's football, but how much information have you absorbed? It's time to put your knowledge to the test in the SHOOT Super Quiz – there are 20 questions worth a total of 40 points!

ANSWERS ON PAGE 47

1 | 1 POINT

Who were the 2022 FA WSL champions?

....

2 | 1 POINT

What is the nationality of Lionesses boss Sarina Wiegman?

....

3 | 2 POINTS

Who won the Scottish Women's Premier League in 2021/22? Rangers or Celtic?

....

4 | 2 POINTS

Who was the PFA Women's Player of the Year for 2022?

Sam Kerr

5 | 2 POINTS

Which club did Scotland star Caroline Weir leave Manchester City for?

....

6 | 1 POINT

Which England player scored six goals and provided five assists at EURO 2022?

....

7 | 2 POINTS

Which team was promoted to the FA WSL in 2022?

....

8 | 1 POINT

True or false?
Ella Toone joined Manchester United from Manchester City.

False

9 — **3 POINTS**

Chelsea beat Manchester City in the 2022 Women's FA Cup Final – but what was the score?

....

10 — **2 POINTS**

Which of these teams has Steph Houghton NOT played for? Leeds United, Durham or Arsenal?

....

11 — **5 POINTS**

Who plays their football at Petershill Park? Glasgow City or Aberdeen?

....

12 — **2 POINTS**

Who are the current women's world champions?

....

13 — **5 POINTS**

Who are the 2022 Welsh champions? Swansea or Cardiff?

....

14 — **3 POINTS**

Where was Beth Mead born? London, Brighton, or Whitby?

....

15 — **1 POINT**

Which WSL team play at Kingsmeadow?

....

16 — **1 POINT**

Who was Manchester United's manager going into the 2022/23 season? Marc Skinner or Casey Stoney?

....

17 — **1 POINT**

Alexia Putellas is regarded as the best player in the world – but which club does she play for?

....

18 — **2 POINTS**

Marta is the record goal-scorer in World Cup history with 17 goals – but which country does she play for?

....

19 — **2 POINTS**

In 2020, USA striker Alex Morgan played 4 league games for which London based WSL club?

....

20 — **1 POINT**

Who did Georgia Stanway join in the summer or 2022? Real Madrid or Bayern Munich?

....

CAPTAIN'S CODE

Here are three inspirational messages from three international captains – using the symbol key on the left, see if you can crack the code to see what they are saying...

A B C D E F
G H I J K
L M N O P
Q R S T U
V W X Y Z

ANSWERS ON PAGE 47

_____ _____　_____ _____ _____

_____　　_____

_____ _____ _____　_____ _____ _____ ,

　,

_____ _____ _____　_____ _____ _____ ,

_____ _____　_____ _____

WENDIE RENARD
FRANCE CAPTAIN

,

_____ _____ _____ _____ ,　_____ _____ _____ _____ ,

_____ _____ _____ _____　_____ _____ _____ _____

_____ _____

ALEXANDRA POPP
GERMANY CAPTAIN

_____ _____ _____　_____ _____ _____ _____ _____ _____ _____ _____

_____

_____ _____ _____ _____ _____　_____ _____ _____ _____

_____ _____ _____ _____ _____　_____ _____ _____ _____

BECKY SAUERBRUNN
USA CAPTAIN

ON THE MOVE!

This season, Lucy Bronze will be playing for Spanish giants FC Barcelona, but can you name the previous five clubs she played for?

ANSWERS ON PAGE 47

1. Man city
2.
3.
4. Liverpool
5. Everton

MILESTONE MOMENTS

There are moments in a player's career that they will never forget – but can you match the eight moments with the correct player?

ANSWERS ON PAGE 47

1 "WINNING THE GOLDEN BOOT AT EURO 2022 WAS A DREAM COME TRUE."

2 "BECOMING ENGLAND'S TOP GOAL-SCORER OF ALL TIME WAS SUCH A PROUD MOMENT FOR ME."

3 "SCORING THE WINNING GOAL THAT WON EURO 2022 IS A MOMENT I WILL NEVER FORGET."

4 "WHEN I CAME TO ENGLAND, I NEVER DREAMED I WOULD BECOME THE FA WSL ALL-TIME TOP SCORER."

5 "INJURY KEPT ME OUT OF EURO 2022, BUT I AM DETERMINED TO WIN BACK MY PLACE AND PLAY IN ANOTHER WORLD CUP."

6 "IT WAS JUST INSTINCT – I'VE NEVER SCORED A BACK-HEEL GOAL BEFORE SO TO DO IT FOR ENGLAND IS SPECIAL!"

7 "I WAS REALLY HAPPY AT MANCHESTER CITY, BUT JOINING BAYERN MUNICH WAS A CHANCE I COULDN'T TURN DOWN."

8 "SCORING THE WINNER IN THE 2022 FA CUP FINAL IS THE SORT OF THING I DREAMED OF AS A KID."

A SAM KERR

B STEPH HOUGHTON

C GEORGIA STANWAY

D ELLEN WHITE

E VIVIANNE MIEDEMA

F ALESSIA RUSSO
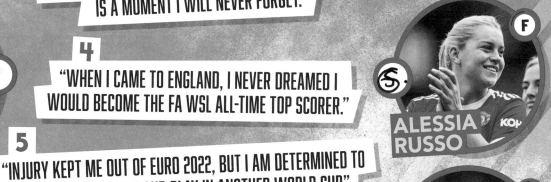

G BETH MEAD

H CHLOE KELLY

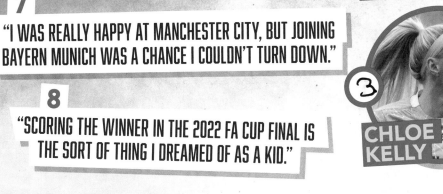

21

DID YOU KNOW?

Facts, trivia, and interesting stats about womens football....

57

CHELSEA'S 57 POINTS FROM 22 GAMES IS A WSL RECORD.

X2

Since 2017, the number of women's team in England has doubled!

RECORD ATTENDANCE

91,553

Barcelona v Real Madrid in 2022.

Heads up! Sam Kerr holds the FA WSL record for most headers scored in one season 9 in 2020/21.

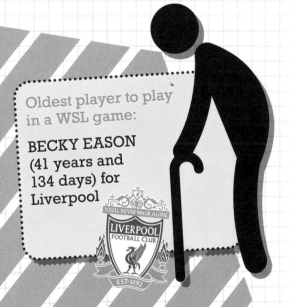

Oldest player to play in a WSL game:

BECKY EASON (41 years and 134 days) for Liverpool

YOUNGEST PLAYER TO APPEAR IN A WSL GAME: LAUREN JAMES

16 YRS, 30 DAYS

(Arsenal vs Everton, 29th September 2017)

LONGEST WSL WINNING STREAK

12 GAMES

ARSENAL & MANCHESTER CITY

BIGGEST WSL WIN
Arsenal 11-1 Bristol City
(2019/20)

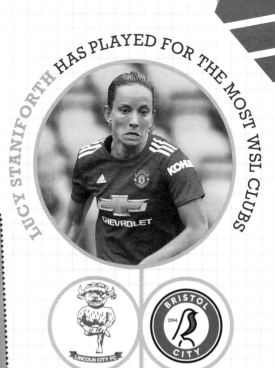

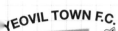

12

The most WSL defeats in succession is held by **Yeovil Town** who lost 12 on the spin in 2017/18.

RECORD WSL ATTENDANCE

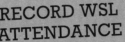

38,262

Spurs v Arsenal in 2019. But expect that to be beaten in 2022/23!

6

2

FEWEST POINTS IN A WSL SEASON
YEOVIL TOWN F.C.

ACHIEVE BY UNITY

2017-18

FASTEST-EVER GOAL SCORED THE WSL
14 SECONDS

JANE ROSS – Manchester City vs Doncaster, 2015/16

Vivianne Miedema's double hat-trick against Bristol City is the most WSL goals scored by one player in one game.

As of summer 2022, Jill Scott's

175

appearances is the most in the FA WSL.

SKILLS WHEEL

You'll need a pair of scissors and a pencil.

If you want to be as good as the stars in this book, you will need to practice tricks and skills everyday. This skills wheel will challenge you and help you improve. What will the skills wheel ask next...?

1 First of all, carefully cut out the skills wheel.

2 Poke a pencil through the middle of the wheel.

3 Your skill wheel is now ready!

4 Now, take it into the garden or backyard with your football and see what the skill wheel wants you to do next!

Ask a grown-up to do this for you or to watch you do the cutting!

PRACTICE
DOING A
RABONA
(Look it up on YouTube)

PRACTICE
SHOTS
AGAINST
THE WALL

PRACTICE
STEPOVERS
10 TIMES

DRIBBLE
UP AND DOWN
THE GARDEN 5 TIMES

PRACTICE DOING
KEEP-UPS
(Try to get more each time!)

PASS THE BALL
6 TIMES
WITH YOUR
WEAKEST FOOT

Make sure you complete the activity on page 26 before you cut out the skills wheel. Or you can photocopy or scan and print the page if you don't want to cut up your book.

SPOT THE DIFFERENCE

Do you have the vision of Georgia Stanway? You'll need it to spot the eight differences between picture A and picture B! See how many you can get.

ANSWERS ON PAGE 47

PICTURE A

PICTURE B

PUT A TICK IN A BOX FOR EACH DIFFERENCE YOU FIND.

PICTURE A

PICTURE B

YOU'RE THE BOSS!

Imagine you've been asked to select a World XI Dream Team. Who will you choose to play?

Put yourself in the shoes of Sarina Wiegman and select your World Dream Team starting XI and six subs for extra back-up if needed! We've selected 34 of the best players in the world across all positions, so make sure you have players who can fill every role. Good luck (you'll need it!)

World XI Dream Team

1. GK Mary Earps
2. DF Lucy Bronz
3. DF Mille Bright
4. DF Steph Houghton
5. DF alsy Lawrence
6. MF Leah Willsom
7. MF Kim Little
8. MF Alexia pucellas
9. FW Sam Fer
10. FW Beth Mead
11. FW Viv ame Miedema

On the bench

12. alessia russo
13. Ellu toov
14. Eilde robuck
15. Fran Fibey
16.
17.

GOALKEEPERS

Christiane Endler (CHI)

Mary Earps (ENG)

Sandra Paños (SPA)

Ellie Roebuck (ENG)

Alyssa Naeher (USA)

DEFENDERS

Amel Marji (FRA)

Lucy Bronze (ENG)

Wendie Renard (FRA)

Steph Houghton (ENG)

Becky Sauerbrunn (USA)

Magdalena Eriksson (SWE)

Millie Bright (ENG)

Fridolina Rolfo (SWE)

Ashley Lawrence (CAN)

Kathrin Hendrich (GER)

Saki Kumagai (JAPAN)

MIDFIELDERS

Alexia Putellas (SPA)

Sara Däbritz (GER)

Lieke Martens (NED)

Kim Little (SCO)

Lindsey Horan (USA)

Pernille Harder (DEN)

Catarina Macario (USA)

Sam Mewis (USA)

Leah Williamson (ENG)

FORWARDS

Megan Rapinoe (USA)

Vivianne Miedema (NED)

Marta (BRA)

Caroline Hansen (NOR)

Fran Kirby (ENG)

Sam Kerr (AUS)

Beth Mead (ENG)

Alexandra Popp (GER)

Caroline Weir (SCO)

STADIUM DESIGNER

It's time to design the football stadium of the future! What will be unique about your stadium?

CAPTION THIS

The SHOOT team have forgotten to add the captions to these seven images. Can you help us by filling in the blanks? Use your imagination. There are no right or wrong answers.

Caption this...

"

"

Caption this...

"

"

Caption this...

"

AMazing

"

Caption this...

" too good "

Caption this...

" Fun "

Caption this...

" Cute "

Caption this...

" Funny "

TOP 10

SUPER TEAMS

So, who are the best women's club teams in the world? SHOOT reveals the sides rated best in the world!

1 OLYMPIQUE LYONNAIS

The most successful club in European history, Lyon have won a record eight Champions League titles so far! They have also won 25 French titles and trophies since 2006 and continue to set the benchmark for women's football.

2 FC BARCELONA

FC Barcelona is the rising force of women's football, assembling a powerful squad full of talented players. They have dominated Spanish football for many years and have now become one of European football's major players, reaching the Champions League final three times in the last four years.

3 WOLFSBURG

For so long, Wolfsburg have been one of women's football's best clubs. They have reached the Champions League final five times, winning it twice and won 16 major titles in Germany. They may not be as dominant as they once were, but they are still a force to be reckoned with.

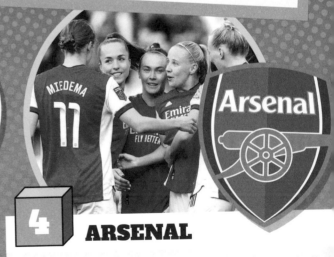

4 ARSENAL

Arsenal's record in English and European football means they are the most successful team in the country. They are the only WSL side to win the Champions League and their incredible success on home soil means they remain the biggest club in the land having been league champions 15 times!

5 CHELSEA

As one of the first English clubs to really invest in their women's team, Chelsea have become one of the best sides in the country. Winners of five WSL titles, they have also won seven domestic trophies and reached the 2021 Champions League final.

6 PARIS SAINT-GERMAIN

Having lived in the shadow of Lyon for so long, PSG have finally broken the spell by winning the French title and cup in recent seasons. Backed by wealthy owners, expect PSG to become the destination for many top players in the years ahead.

7 BAYERN MUNICH

Like PSG, Bayern Munich have long lived in the shadow of a powerful rival – but times are changing. Bayern are determined to prove there is more to women's football in Germany than Wolfsburg and recent investment has seen them improve year on year. Expect big things from Bayern as well!

8 MANCHESTER CITY

Though their side has existed for many years, it wasn't until 2016 that City first won the WSL. Since 2014 when the club relaunched, they have won seven domestic cups and they have been runners-up in the league an incredible six times in the past seven seasons.

9 ATLETICO MADRID

A side who has produced many top players, and have been one of Spain's most competitive teams for a many years. With growth of Spanish football in the past couple of years, Atletico are well placed to challenge Barca and Real Madrid in the years ahead.

10 MANCHESTER UNITED

Since forming in 2018, United have made steady progress each season in the WSL. Significant squad investment has seen them get stronger each year and expect them to challenge at home and in Europe over the next few years.

PUZZLE PITCH

ANSWERS ON PAGE 48

TRANSFER TRACKER

Can you name the player just by their last four transfers?

A Arsenal → Notts County FC → Birmingham City → Manchester City

Name:

B Bristol City → Reading Football Club → W (Wolfsburg) → Manchester United

Name:

C Bristol City → Liverpool → Manchester City → Real Madrid

Name:

FAMILIAR FACES

Can you name the footballers in these close-up photos?

C

B

A

CLUB CRISIS

Below are three scrambled WSL clubs – can you figure out which sides they are by unscrambling the letters?

SHE LACE ....

A NO ILL VAST ....

DEAR GIN ....

Welcome to the Puzzle Pitch! Dribble around each mini puzzle until you get into the box and bury the ball in the back of the net!

GETTING SHIRTY

Which FA WSL clubs do these shirts belong to?

A
AIA
....

B
CASTORE
CAZOO
earch. Drive. Smile.
....

C
standard charte
....

CROSS COUNTRY

Draw the correct line to link each player to the country they play for.

Alexia Putellas

Khadija Shaw

Jen Beattie

JAMAICA

SCOTLAND

SPAIN

GOAL! →

WHO ARE YA?!

Can you guess the mystery player from the three clues below?

A

Clue 1: I play in goal for Manchester City and England.
Clue 2: My best mate is Chloe Kelly.
Clue 3: I represented Great Britain at the 2020 Olympics.
....

B

Clue 1: I am the top World Cup goal-scorer of all time.
Clue 2: I wear the No.10 shirt for Brazil.
Clue 3: I play my club football for Orlando Pride.
....

C

Clue 1: I was joint-top scorer at EURO 2022.
Clue 2: I missed the EURO 2022 final with injury I picked up during the warm-up.
Clue 3: I play my club football in my home country for Wolfsburg.
....

All you need to know about...

THE LIONESSES

Facts, stats, and trivia on the European champions...

FIRST ROAR!

The Lionesses played their first official game in 1972 against Scotland, coming from 2–0 down to win 3–2 with Sylvia Gore scoring the very first England goal.

FIFA WOMEN'S WORLD CUP AU 20 NZ 23

GETTING CLOSER!

The Lionesses have qualified for the FIFA Women's World Cup on five occasions. Our best performances so far were fourth in 2019 and third in 2015. The next World Cup is in 2023 in Australia and New Zealand.

HOPE FOR THE BEST!

The Lionesses were managed by men from 1972 to 1998 — until the legend that is Hope Powell took over as England's first woman boss in 1998 and stayed in the hot seat for 15 years! By the time she stepped down in 2013, Hope had managed 169 England games!

IT CAME HOME - FINALLY!

The Lionesses EURO 2022 success was the first major trophy for a senior England football team since the men's team won the World Cup in 1966 — that's 56 long years we had to wait!

BORN IN 2012!

England Women's team officially became the 'Lionesses' in 2012 when the Football Association's digital marketing team came up with name to give the women's team their own identity, separate to England men's world famous nickname of 'Three Lions'.

RECORD CROWD

England fans packed Wembley for the EURO 2022 final with the 87,192 crowd breaking all previous records for fans attending a women's international. FAN-tastic!

ATTENDANCE
87,192
RO TOURNAMENT R
Hisense

CAPTAIN FANTASTIC

Though injury cost Steph Houghton a place at EURO 2022 and the captain's armband, she remains the Lionesses' very own captain fantastic — Manchester City star Houghton led England from 2014 to 2022 — longer than anyone in Lionesses history.

MOST CAPS

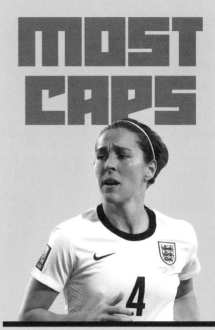

Fara Williams is the most-capped Lioness to date - she won an incredible 172 caps between 2001 and 2019, scoring 40 goals. Jill Scott, who played in the EURO 2022 final against Germany, made 161 appearances before announcing her retirement in August 2022.

MOST GOALS

Ellen White is England's all-time record goal-scorer. After EURO 2022, the Manchester City striker was on 52 goals from 113 appearances and replaced Kelly Smith (46 goals) at the top of the list in 2022.

KIRBY

BRONZE OR SCOTT ?

ANSWERS ON PAGE 48

Do you know your England EURO 2022 superstars? Read the 15 facts below and tell us whether they are about Lucy Bronze, Jill Scott or Fran Kirby.

If you think the answer is **Fran Kirby** - Put the letter **K** in the circle.

If you think the answer is **Lucy Bronze** - Put the letter **B** in the circle.

If you think the answer is **Jill Scott** - Put the letter **S** in the circle.

1 I own a coffee shop in Manchester.

2 One of my middle names is Tough.

3 With 71 goals by the end of the 2021/22, I am my club's record goal-scorer.

4 I once worked in a pizza takeaway

5 In 2020 I was named FIFA Best Women's Player of the Year.

6 I scored my first England goals against Sweden in 2014.

7 In my club career, I have signed for the same club on two occasions

8 I have played for Sunderland, Manchester City, Everton, and Aston Villa.

9 I began my career with Reading.

11 My hometown has a team that is in England but plays in the Scottish league!

10 I am the only player on the list to have NOT played for Sunderland.

12 In my club career, I have played for two teams in Europe so far.

13 Only one Lioness has won more caps than I have.

14 I am the only player on this list to have won the Champions League.

15 A former England manager nicknamed me 'Mini Messi' – but I don't like it!

THE 50/50 QUIZ

Can you correctly answer these 10 questions? You have at 50/50 chance of getting it right! Do you know the answer, or do you feel lucky...?

ANSWERS ON PAGE 48

1 AS OF SUMMER 2022, WHO HAS MORE USA CAPS?

MEGAN RAPINOE

ALEX MORGAN

2 WHO HAS SCORED MORE FA WSL HAT-TRICKS?

SAM KERR

VIVIANNE MIEDEMA

3 HOW FAST WAS THE QUICKEST FA WSL GOAL?

8 SECONDS 00:08

12 SECONDS 00:12

4 WHAT IS JAMAICA STRIKER KHADIJA SHAW'S NICKNAME?

BUNNY

KITTY

5
WHO HAS WON MORE WORLD CUPS?

USA

BRAZIL

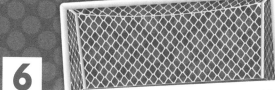

6
WHAT IS THE NICKNAME FOR HITTING THE BALL INTO THE TOP CORNER OF THE GOAL?

TOP BANANA

TOP BINS

7
WITH WHAT FOOT DID CHLOE KELLY SCORE THE WINNING GOAL OF THE EURO 2022 FINAL AGAINST GERMANY?

RIGHT FOOT

LEFT FOOT

8
WHO DOES RISING SCOTTISH STAR TEGAN BOWIE PLAY FOR?

CELTIC

RANGERS

9
AT 16 YEARS AND 258 DAYS OLD, WHO IS THE FA WSL YOUNGEST EVER SCORER?

ELLA TOONE

LAUREN HEMP

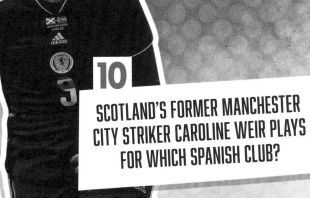

10
SCOTLAND'S FORMER MANCHESTER CITY STRIKER CAROLINE WEIR PLAYS FOR WHICH SPANISH CLUB?

BARCELONA

REAL MADRID

TOP 10

WSL RISING STARS

SHOOT scouts have been scoring the WSL for the best talent and have identified 10 players to watch during the 2022/23 season...

1 MARY FOWLER

The 19 year-old joined Manchester City from Montpellier in 2022. With two major tournaments under her belt already, the Australia international is one of the Matildas brightest stars to emerge since Sam Kerr and is expected to be a big hit in the FA WSL.

2 ELLA TOONE

Ella announced her arrival on the international stage during EURO 2022 as the Lionesses' super sub. She is expected to take on the mantle of England's main striker over the next few seasons now Ellen White has retired from playing.

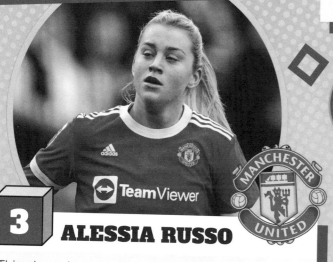

3 ALESSIA RUSSO

This player became household name in Europe after her incredible EURO 2022 back-heel goal against Sweden. The powerful forward is improving year-on-year with her technique and finishing ability and is expected to lead the Lionesses forward line for many years to come.

4 JESSIE FLEMING

Although she has 100 caps for her country, the Canadian midfielder is emerging star in the WSL. She made her debut for Canada aged just 15 and already has a wealth of experience – and she keeps getting better!

5 ONA BATLLE

Ona has quickly become one of the WSL's most coveted defenders. The Spain international is quick and dynamic and was voted into the PFA Team of the Year for her consistency with the Reds – expect her to kick on again in 2022/23.

6 MAYA LE TISSIER

The England Under-23 defender was snapped up by Manchester United in the summer of 2022 and is expected to flourish with the Reds. The athletic youngster is expected to progress to the Lionesses senior set-up before too long.

7 HANNAH HAMPTON

One of an exciting crop of young English goalkeepers, Hannah began life as a forward for Villarreal's academy and had to undergo several eye operations as a child – so she has proved already she is a fighter and has her eyes on being the Lionesses No.1 in the near future.

8 LILY WOODHAM

Lily moved to Reading in 2018 followed by a quick spell on loan with Charlton. She returned to Reading and has gone from strength to strength. A Welsh international, she is quick and agile and has a bright future.

9 LAUREN HEMP

One of the WSL's most exciting talents, many believe Lauren will go on and become one of England's best footballers in 2022/23. A star of EURO 2022, she is also one of the best players in a star-studded Manchester City team with whom she hit 16 goals in 31 games last season.

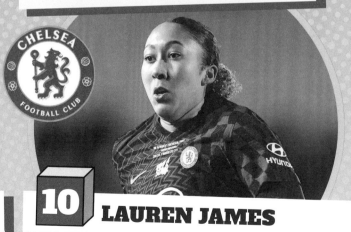

10 LAUREN JAMES

The sister of Chelsea star Reece James, Lauren joined her brother at Stamford Bridge in 2021 from Manchester United. A prolific goal-scorer for the Reds, she is expected to challenge the galaxy of attacking talent Chelsea have in 2022/23.

PRE-MATCH SMOOTHIE

What better before training or a big match than a healthy, energy-boosting smoothie? SHOOT have researched the best of the best to create a smoothie that ticks all the boxes and is super easy to make.

First things first, get an adult to help you use the blender and chop the banana – or at least watch you while you're creating the magic!

Pre-match smoothie

(serves 2 – so one for you and one for your teammate!)

YOU WILL NEED:

- 2 cups skimmed milk
- 2 bananas
- 1/2 cup plain yoghurt
- 1/2 tsp ground cinnamon
- 6 ice cubes
- 1 tbs honey

METHOD:

1 Place all ingredients in a blender, with the honey being the last ingredient added.

2 Blend in the blender until all ingredients are smooth – hence the name smoothie!

3 Serve in two tall beakers with a shake of cinnamon on top and a slice of banana to garnish. Job done! (You can put it in a flask to keep cool until just before, during or after the game).

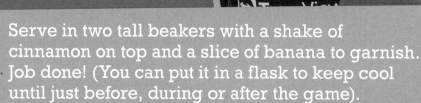

ANSWERS

5 SCRAMBLED STARS!

1. Lauren Hemp
2. Mary Earps
3. Ella Toone
4. Ellen White
5. Demi Stokes
6. Alex Greenwood

8-9 SPOT THE BALL

GAME 1: Ball A
GAME 2: Ball B
GAME 3: Ball F
GAME 4: Ball C

10 MAGIC MEGAN

Balls C, D and E

11 CHAMPIONS OF EUROPE

16-17 SHOOT SUPER QUIZ

1. Chelsea
2. Dutch
3. Rangers
4. Sam Kerr
5. Real Madrid
6. Beth MEad
7. Liverpool
8. True
9. 3-2
10. Durham
11. Glasgow City

12. USA
13. Swansea City
14. Whitby
15. Chelsea
16. Marc Skinner
17. Barcelona
18. Brazil
19. Tottenham Hotspur
20. Bayern Munich

18-19 CAPTAIN'S CODE

WENDIE RENARD
"If you dream you can do it, you can"

ALEXANDRA POPP
"Never, never, never give up"

BECKY SAUERBRUNN
"Big journeys begin with small steps"

20 ON THE MOVE

1. Manchester City
2. Lyon
3. Manchester City
4. Liverpool
5. Everton

21 MILESTONE MOMENTS

1. Beth Mead
2. Ellen White
3. Chloe Kelly
4. Vivianne Miedema
5. Steph Houghton
6. Alessia Russo
7. Georgia Stanway
8. Sam Kerr

26-27 SPOT THE DIFFERENCE

ANSWERS

36-37 PUZZLE PITCH

TRANSFER TRACKER
A: Ellen White
B: Mary Earps
C: Caroline Weir

CLUB CRISIS
Chelsea
Aston Villa
Reading

FAMILIAR FACES
A: Alex Morgan
B: Sam Kerr
C: Vivianne Miedema

GETTING SHIRTY
A: Tottenham Hotspur
B: Aston Villa
C: Liverpool

WHO ARE YA?
A: Ellie Roebuck
B: Marta
C: Alexandra Popp

CROSS COUNTRY
Alexia Putellas - Spain
Khadija Shaw - Jamaica
Jen Beattie - Scotland

40-41 KIRBY, BRONZE OR SCOTT

1. Scott
2. Bronze
3. Kirby
4. Bronze
5. Bronze
6. Kirby
7. Bronze
8. Scott
9. Kirby
10. Kirby
11. Bronze
12. Bronze
13. Scott
14. Bronze
15. Kirby

42-43 THE 50/50 QUIZ

1. Alex Morgan
2. Vivianne Miedema
3. 12 seconds
4. Bunny
5. USA
6. Top bins
7. Right foot
8. Celtic
9. Lauren Hemp
10. Real Madrid